MW00627650

Monk of All Faiths

Inspired by *The Prophet*

Gudjon Bergmann

Dedication

To my dad

The Monk Arrives

He was known as the monk of all faiths. For over forty years, he had traveled the world, staying in monasteries, temples, churches, caves, tents, and synagogues, with gurus, sufis, yogis, mystics, shamans, and religious families alike. Like a chameleon, he took on the attributes of their traditions, prayed, ate, meditated, and served as they did, living each religion to the best of his ability.

He had never written anything, never given interviews, never broadcast his message, yet word of his peaceful interactions with people of all faiths had spread. Those who had heard about him were curious. Why did he go on this journey? How did he get along with people? What had he learned?

On this day, the monk had agreed to answer questions about his journey for the first time. A small group of men and women had gathered in a spacious retreat center in the mountains, eager to hear what he had to say.

There was no pomp or ceremony when the monk arrived. He was wearing a simple polo shirt and slacks, and with his tan skin, short-cropped gray beard and balding head, the monk could have blended into any crowd.

As he sat down in a chair centered on a slightly elevated stage, many in the audience bowed their heads in reverence.

The monk greeted them with his hands in prayer pose. He spoke in a gentle voice and addressed the audience with a simple: "Hello brothers and sisters. Thank you for coming."

He was ready for his first question.

Perennial

A young man said: "We appreciate your presence here today and are glad to meet you. Tell us, why did you choose to live with people of all faiths? Why not settle on one path?"

A smile spread across the monk's face as he joyfully replied: "Perennial. That was the word, the idea, that started my journey. In nature, perennial herbs and flowers bloom repeatedly. They remain in the earth, then blossom and show their true colors when certain conditions are met.

Growing up, I traveled the world with my parents and was around people of all faiths. We attended churches and temples in busy trading hubs where the monks and priests read equally from the Bible, Gita, Koran, and Torah. I knew that each religion had its own culture, and that each book read differently, yet, instinctively, I also felt like something deeper tied them together.

When I first came upon the idea of perennialism in my late teens, it felt like a continuation of my life experiences. Curiosity overtook me. Could the same esoteric truths be present in all of the world's religions and show their colors when the right conditions were met? Merely asking the question was exhilarating.

My thirst was such that I read all the scriptures in search of clues. I scoured through the words of Moses, Krishna, Christ, Buddha, the prophet Muhammad, peace be upon him, Bahaullah, and Guru Nanak. I explored first nations wisdom from Africa, Scandinavia, America, and Australia, and read books by masters and saints from every tradition. Their teachings, stories, and methods fed my soul, and I found considerable overlaps—but something was still missing."

The monk paused for effect.

"Then it struck me. I was like a traveler at a train station who spent all his time reading travel brochures and never went on a trip. Reading about the beauty of waterfalls in Kenya was well and good, but I could never appreciate their full beauty unless I saw them with my own eyes. I needed to experience the lived reality of religion to find the perennial truths on my own.

In that spirit, I reached out to a Christian monastery in France and asked if I could stay with them for six months. They agreed. During that time, I learned more about lived Christianity than I had from any book. After my stay was over, I made the same request of a Buddhist monastery in Kuala Lumpur. They also agreed. And so it continued.

Within three years, I did not need to make requests. People saw the value of what I was attempting to do, and I was offered to live at places of worship, monasteries, and with families of different religious persuasions all over the world. From Texas to Norway, Japan to Argentina, India to Israel, it seemed like everyone wanted to show me the beauty of their beliefs.

In every instance, I took on the attributes of their religions. I prayed, ate, meditated, and served as they did. I took part in their ceremonies. I lived each religion to the best of my ability. And just like bluebonnets, the perennial truths showed themselves to me each and every time.

Reading religious texts had prepared me well, but it was only through lived experience that I came to feel those truths, live them, experience them.

My perennial journey has now lasted four decades. It has become my life's mission, the reason why I took the vows of a monk. Today, as I answer your questions, I hope to share some of the insights that I have gathered along the way. Please remember that words of wisdom are only seeds. It is through application and action that perennial seeds sprout, grow, and flower."

All Faiths

A middle-aged woman said: "You say you are of all faiths… but I just can't believe that. Please, be truthful. What is your religion?"

The monk responded with consideration: "I was not born to a single race, which is why I belong to the human family. I was not raised in a single country, which is why the Earth is my home. I have prayed with monks, nuns, priests, swamis, gurus, families, and masters of all faiths. Each one of those faiths has spoken to me in some way.

In my search, two perennial seeds have sprouted in all circumstances—the principles of *oneness* and *goodness*. They have come to constitute my religion."

He closed his eyes as he spoke.

"Oneness is the fundamental nature of the universe. Everything is connected to everything else.

We cannot see it with our eyes. We cannot feel it with our skin. Only when we dwell in silence and unveil the deepest recesses of our consciousness can we come to this ultimate realization.

Our essential nature is one.

My Buddhist friends call it Emptiness.

My Hindu brothers and sisters call it Brahman.

My Christian family calls it God or the Holy Spirit.

Oneness is found beyond duality, beyond the world of lights and shadows, beyond words and forms, beyond names and shapes. Oneness is the ever-present and unchanging essence of everything. It has been revealed to sincere seekers of every faith through practices such as silence, contemplative prayer, and meditation."

During a short period of stillness, the monk appeared to reach a wholly peaceful state. Then he opened his eyes and continued.

"Of course, such an experience of oneness is not the lived daily reality for most people—even those of us who have tasted the sweet essence of unity.

The relative truth is more mundane because the created world is perceived as dualistic by all of us. Despite the underlying oneness, everything appears separate from everything else. This perception of duality is a powerful veiling force. Because of it, we feel detached, alone, and at odds with each other, even at odds with ourselves.

That is where the perennial principle of goodness comes in. Its purpose is to help us create harmony in societies big and small, to create harmony within, to help us choose between good and bad in the realm of duality.

To this end, every faith tradition has emphasized the cultivation of love, compassion, generosity, and kindness. Such expressions of goodness are not easy to come by. In the dualistic world, our animal nature is strong. As humans—an advanced species of mammals—we are intensely tribal, sexual, possessive, and more prone to violence than any other species on Earth.

Thusly, the values of compassion, fairness, justice, love, forgiveness, and generosity are not given. To bloom, they must be nurtured from within and supported from without, preferably in a community. Only an overflowing cup of love can truly be shared with another.

These principles of *oneness* and *goodness*—perennial truths that can be found in all of the world's wisdom traditions and religions—comprise the essence of my faith. They are expressed through practices such as meditation, contemplation, service, compassion, and love. Therefore, as long as I am traveling in the direction of oneness and goodness, any tradition will serve as my vehicle."

He paused as a new question came to him.

"Now, should everyone embrace all faiths equally as I do?" he continued. "My answer to that question is much simpler: Only if it appeals to them.

Most people will probably fair better if they focus on being authentic children of their own traditions while simultaneously honoring all of them.

For instance, if someone has a strong connection with Christ, that person should focus on being an authentic Christian. Christianity is primarily a religion of goodness. If someone truly embraces and embodies that faith with all their heart and all their mind and all their soul, that person will be of more service to the world than if he or she would try to embrace ideas that feel foreign."

God

An older man said: "My faith is shaken. Tell me, do you still believe in God?"

The monk replied gently: "God. That is such an interesting word for the Great Mystery. God. A word derived from ancient English, meaning *good*.

Many words have been used to describe the Divine throughout the ages, yet every attempt to finish the sentence "God is..." has put human limitations on the indescribable. We cannot possibly define that which lies beyond our senses, thoughts, and emotions with a single label.

The Hindu swamis taught me that their gods and goddesses are merely reflections of Brahman, the One without a Second.

My Sufi brothers describe Allah—which literally means *The God*—with a multitude of different adjectives in their prayers, each signifying an important aspect of the Divine.

This practice is common in Islam. In one Muslim household where I stayed, they had a picture on the wall with the ninety-nine names of God in Arabic.

Granted, not all religions have gone down that path. Most Buddhist traditions, for instance, simply refuse to speculate about God.

Yet, we humans are philosophers at heart.

We speculate.

Where did we come from? Where are we going? What is our purpose? Who created us? Why? These questions are at the heart of every religion."

The monk smiled as if he had just thought of a funny joke.

"Now ponder this paradox. I've described my religion to you as founded on the principles of oneness and goodness. Yet, I find that I enter into a realm of spiritual poverty when I try to define God as either One or Love or both.

In one way or another, God is the answer to every single 'why' question that human beings have failed to answer throughout the ages and have still not resolved despite technological advances.

Why does the sun shine? we ask.

Because it is a planet of molten lava that produces warmth through volcanic action, the scientist answers. Yet, even if he thinks otherwise, he has not answered a 'why' question but rather a 'how' question. He has explained 'how' the sun shines, not 'why' it shines.

Looking closely, the scientist's dilemma represents the truth about all 'why' questions. In fact, we can answer 'how' questions all the way back to the Big Bang, but we cannot answer a single 'why' question. We can answer 'how' a baby is born but not 'why,' 'how' the stars align but not 'why,' 'how' coffee is made but not 'why' there exists such a thing as coffee.

As I understand it, God is the why. The Alpha and the Omega. The beginning and the end. We could use every word from every language to describe God, yet we would still fail.

The prophets who've contemplated God deeply have marveled at the sheer majesty of what they have discovered. All of them would admit that they have seen but a fragment."

The excitement in his voice grew.

"In the Bhagavad Gita, Arjuna recoils when God tries to reveal his entire majesty. The same thing happens in the Bible. One great Islamic scholar said: "Whatever you think God is, know he is more than that."

The human mind is too feeble to comprehend the totality of God.

We are like a flea on a dog's body, thinking that the dog is the entire universe.

We are like a fish that longs to know the ocean. The ocean is its habitat. It flows through the fish, and the fish flows through it. Yet, the fish can never rise above the ocean and observe it.

We are thirsty fish swimming in the ocean of God."

The monk took a sip of his water, as if to underline what he had just said, then continued in a soft voice.

"And so, because we cannot know the entirety of God, we latch onto aspects that we can relate to. A heart gives us an insight into how a human body works. Yet, the heart, however necessary, is not the entire body. We can connect to the heart of God, but let us never reduce God to a mere heart. God is more than that.

I believe in God in the same way that a fish believes in the ocean. God is the very reason for my existence, the hidden order of things in the universe. God is part of me, and I am part of God. That is the definition I have come to embrace. And in my commitment to all faiths, I accept every word that attempts to convey the Great Mystery."

Spirit

A young woman said: "I am not very religious. In fact, I belong to the fastest-growing group in the world, people who are spiritual but not religious. Could you talk to us about Spirit?"

The monk responded with enthusiasm: "Yes. What you call Spirit has been called many names. Self. Soul. Atman. Essence. The Witness. Pure Awareness.

But, as with God, these are only words.

The word jasmine does not discharge an aroma. It labels a flower that emits a pleasing fragrance. Similarly, the term Spirit is meaningless unless it points to something real. Yet, when we look around, we cannot find Spirit.

Is it inside?

Is it outside?

Is it everywhere?

Is it nowhere?

In many ways, Spirit is like electricity. We do not see it, and yet it powers the world around us. The mystics understood this. They saw beyond the world of light and shadows.

In the Upanishads, Spirit is described as that which makes the tongue speak but cannot be spoken by the tongue; that which makes the mind think but cannot be thought by the mind; that which makes the eye see but cannot be seen by the eye; that which makes the ear hear but cannot be heard by the ear; that which makes you draw breath but cannot be drawn by your breath.

We cannot see it. We cannot speak it. We cannot hear it. We cannot think it. But we can experience it.

All the faiths have devised religious practices to that end, to help us unveil the unseen. From Christian mystics to Yoga masters, Sufi saints, Jewish Kabbalists, Zen Buddhists, and beyond, all have devised techniques. Their methods may vary, but they all agree on one thing. For Spirit to be realized, the body, emotions, and intellect must be *transcended*.

Transcendence is that most beautiful of spiritual concepts. It means to go beyond. Beyond the mind and body. Beyond duality, time, and space. Beyond language, shapes, and forms. Transcending means letting go of all preconceived notions. We have to stop thinking that Spirit is either 'in here' or 'out there.' Spirit cannot be reduced to a location or an idea.

Masters of all ages have tried to tell us this.

Follow our methods, they have said, but don't focus on our methods.

Listen to our words, they have said, but don't take our words literally.

See where we are pointing, they have said, but don't look at our fingers.

Without going anywhere, they have said, go beyond your limitations.

Transcend while you remain.

For those who persist, it truly is a beautiful experience. The essence is unborn, undying, everlasting. Fire does not burn it, and water does not wet it.

It is always present. It does not change."

The monk paused to reminisce.

"I can testify that after a direct experience of Spirit, life will never be the same. It is like the spiritual seeker has been living in a darkened room until that point, afraid of a snake curled up in the corner. When the lights are turned on, there is an immediate realization that the snake was really a rope. Even if the lights are turned off after that, the seeker will never again be afraid that the rope is a snake.

Turning on the light for a moment.

That is temporary enlightenment.

Permanent enlightenment is trickier. Only those who repeatedly turn on the light will reach a state of enduring illumination.

Thankfully, all faiths have produced mystics who have shown us the way. If we truly want to know Spirit, we must take the road less traveled and follow in their footsteps. The pathway may be overgrown in places, and sometimes we may stumble around, but every step will be richly rewarded. As we inch closer to our destination, a direct transcendental perception will serve as our scent. And just like the smell of jasmine, even if we cannot see it, our experience will tell us that it is real."

Destructive Emotions

A middle-aged man said: "I have had a hard time dealing with anger and fear lately. What do the wisdom traditions say about dealing with destructive emotions?"

The monk responded somberly: "We all have to deal with destructive emotions. That is a part of being human. You might not think it, but I was an angry young man. I constantly railed against the injustices of the world. There were so many. I felt like the anger was completely justified, but it was eating me up from the inside.

I carried that anger with me long after I started my perennial journey, repressed it, pretended it wasn't there, hoped that no one would see the pain it was causing me.

It wasn't until I stayed at a Tibetan monastery that I found a new way. They knew anger and injustice. Banished from their home country. How could they be so happy, so compassionate?

The answer? Transmutation.

Instead of going to extremes by fully expressing their rage through violent action or repressing it in the darkest recesses of their minds, they had learned to transmute that energy into something beneficial, to funnel it into action and compassion.

The monks taught me to think of anger like a raging river that would tear through everything in its path unless it was tamed. Only then did I realize that I had tried to build a dam with no outlet. Destructive emotions were relentlessly battering the dam, and cracks were showing. I needed to reduce the pressure, or else it would break."

There was palpable relief in the monk's voice.

"The first outlet they proposed was *action*. I could use volatile energy to propel me to do good in the world. This helped me make a deeper commitment to the perennial path of goodness. Like the founder of Methodism, I decided to do all the good I could, in all the places I could, at all the times I could, to all the people I could, as long as I could.

The second outlet was *forgiveness*. Gandhi taught us that the core principle of nonviolent resistance was to never hate the doer, only resist the action. When Christ uttered the words, "Father forgive them for they know not what they do," he demonstrated the power of forgiveness. He was asking his Father to forgive the doers as they were executing him. In the same way, when the Buddha told his followers that being angry was like picking up a piece of coal to throw it at another person, he was saying that the person holding the coal was the only one who got burned. Forgiveness is letting go of that coal, letting go of the pain, anger, and hatred that we carry within us.

The third outlet was *awareness*. In every spiritual home, temple, and church I stayed in, there was always a daily ritualized routine that included awareness of those destructive emotions.

In meditation, we calmed the waves in the mind.

In prayer, we asked that those destructive emotions be taken from us and we be forgiven for any trespasses.

In service, we directed energy toward doing something good.

In contemplation, reading, and listening, we asked ourselves what the prophets would do in our situation.

All of these traditions served the purpose of increasing awareness, which is one reason why they have survived and thrived through millennia."

There was real joy in the monk's voice as he concluded.

"These three outlets changed my relationship with destructive emotions. I no longer feared them. Instead, I learned to see them as energy. I listened to what the emotions of fear, anger, resentment, and irritation were telling me, then I funneled that energy into suitable outlets. Like with the transmutation of coal into a diamond, I learned to apply the appropriate pressure and transform what initially appeared destructive into something valuable."

Morality

A middle-aged man said: "The world appears to be a hard place to navigate without a moral compass. What do the traditions say about morality?"

The monk answered thoughtfully: "Morality is an intriguing subject, indeed. Why is this? Why do the religious and nonreligious alike put an emphasis on morality?

I guess it is because anthropologists have yet to find a culture or tribe anywhere on Earth that has operated without restraints. If humans ever endorsed total permissiveness, that social structure has left no remnants.

We are a strange mix of aspirations and primal instincts; better angels and the animal within. The primitive nature of the body is lustful, greedy, and prone to violence... yet human beings are also wired for cooperation. A healthy human being will thrive in a loving and cooperative environment.

So, when we speak of morality, we are speaking of two things.

One is *restriction,* trying to rein in everything that can cause internal and external damage, from angry and fearful emotions to greedy, violent, and lustful behavior.

The other is *aspiration,* cultivating the seeds of goodness, including love, compassion, generosity, and kindness.

Most religious systems were created hundreds or even thousands of years ago. Back then, human behavior was considerably different from what it is today. There was much more violence and strife. Under those circumstances, a moral emphasis was placed on restrictions and restraint. No lying, no stealing, no murdering, and, because it so disturbed the peace in society and usually led to violence, no adultery. All faiths created similar boundaries.

Today, many of those same restraints are found in the justice system, making us take them for granted.

Aspirations are the opposite. Depending on traditions, practitioners are encouraged to honor their elders, respect their teachers, be good, do good, give with joy, cultivate faith, nurture love, and so on.

These two different approaches to morality are perennial because they are found in some shape or form in all religions. Yet, interestingly enough, they have also created two common problems.

Those partial to restrictions have sometimes gone overboard in their designation of restrictive behaviors. They have felt that a moral life can only be achieved by 'not doing.' This has meant that natural behaviors, such as sex and eating, have often been completely restricted. Sadly, this approach always causes a backlash because natural elements can only be guided, never repressed. No matter how high a barricade you build, it will either overflow or break if there is no outlet—just as with destructive emotions.

On the other side, some of those who've been partial to aspirations have become oblivious to the animal within and started preaching theologies of holiness, claiming that the so-called lower human dispositions can be completely transcended. They have mischaracterized the temporary transcendence of the mortal world as a fixed state that can be maintained. Regrettably, the history of religion is full of stories of priests and gurus who have fallen from grace because they succumbed to the lower urges they imagined to have vanquished."

Sadness came over the monk, his eyes drifting. After a moment, he shook his head to break the reverie, smiled, and continued.

"Granted, not everyone has been so blind. Our Zen friends have long reminded us that we have to continue to chop wood and carry water after enlightenment. We are mortal and subject to human limitations. Even after we experience the Divine, we are still comprised of dirt.

Morality, therefore, is a continual dance between these two forces of restrictions and aspirations. That is the paradox.

On one end, we must honor the needs of the animal within and create suitable outlets, yet never allow those urges to assume complete control of our lives.

On the other end, we can aspire and work towards becoming better than we are without falling into the trap of claiming perfection. Even if we temporarily transcend the flesh, we still live in the flesh."

Love

A young woman said: "As someone who really values what you have described as goodness, I am curious, what have the wisdom traditions taught you about love?"

The monk smiled broadly as he answered: "Love. Yes. All the scriptures have something to say about love. The Buddhists remind us that hatred can never put an end to hatred — love alone can. Christ asked us to love our neighbors as ourselves. The Hindu swamis told me that true love is divine, without condition.

Here is the curious thing, though. Despite all the beautiful words written on the subject, most of what I have learned about love, I have learned from the people I have stayed with, not from books. Observing their lives, I have realized that love is not merely a feeling. It is a call to action, a willingness to give, support, and help others.

From my mother, I learned that love was being there in times of distress.

From my father, I learned that love was firm preparation for the difficulties of the world.

From the Christian monks I lived with in France, I learned that love was feeding the poor and homeless, not asking anything in return.

From the Hindu family I lived with in India, I learned that love was taking care of the elderly and allowing them to age in grace.

From my Muslim friends in Turkey, I learned that love was sharing a meal with a stranger, inviting him into the home and offering exceptional hospitality.

From a priest I worked with in Pennsylvania, I learned that love was helping prisoners find dignity through work after they had served their sentence.

From the humanist family I lived with in Germany, I learned that love was thinking of the good of the planet with every action, from purchasing to consumption to recycling.

From a group of interfaith chaplains I worked with at a children's cancer hospital, I learned that love was the gift of presence, sitting with people through their pain instead of trying to fix suffering with empty words.

From the Buddhist monks I stayed with in Australia, I learned that love was supporting people through their emotional pain as they tried to steady their minds in meditation."

The monk's face glowed as he recounted these examples.

"All the love-practitioners I've been around have had one thing in common. They put other people's wellbeing before their own. They were willing to give of their time and energy unselfishly without asking anything in return.

And so, even though love is the most written about, sung about, and cinematized feeling in the world, it also appears to be the most widely misunderstood.

Passions for procreation may ignite, but love can only be sustained with heart and hands. From everything I have observed, love is doing."

Religion and War

A young man said: "You speak well of all the faiths traditions. How do you explain the role of religion in war?"

The monk bowed his head in sadness and answered: "Regrettably, religion has been at the center of too many wars. Of course, saying that offers a deceptively simple narrative—especially since those in power have regularly misused religious teachings to galvanize their people against others—yet, the entanglement between the two does leave us with an important question: Why has religion so often become the vehicle for war?

The best answer I found came from the time I spent with a Vedantic guru in the Himalayas. He talked about the forces of *raga* (strong attraction) and *dvesha* (aversion to the opposite) in the human mind and how they could distort our sense of right and wrong. Once an attraction to a certain practice or belief was formed, he said, the mind automatically generated a subtle aversion. As the attraction increased, so did the aversion. With time, love for one thing could cause hate for another."

The monk illustrated this by pulling his hands apart like he was holding a rubber band, demonstrating one extreme with his right hand and the other with his left.

"It's a natural human tendency. The more we like something, the more we dislike the opposite. And so, because the religion of goodness focuses intently on virtuous practices, values and lays out what it means to be good, opposite beliefs and practices can be branded as wrong, especially as righteousness increases. In the most extreme manifestation of this principle, people of one faith can be convinced that people of another faith are evil. Then, fighting a war is not only justified — it becomes the right thing to do.

Fear and antipathy are powerful motivators. The universal forces of attraction and aversion pose challenges to all religions and need to be moderated rather than fueled. As the Vedantic guru was fond of saying: "Religion is like a cow. It gives milk, but it also kicks." I have chosen to focus more on extracting the milk… but all of us need to learn to guard against the kicking. Religions are only as good as the people who practice them."

Multiplying Goodness

An older woman said: "I also focus on extracting the milk. My religious life is all about service. Can you talk more about how you have experienced goodness in the faith traditions?

The monk responded merrily: "Religious communities offer a tremendous sense of belonging and are often organized around selfless service. They give people places to gather, grieve, heal, and rejoice.

I have endless examples of how goodness shows up in different faith communities.

The sweeping sadhu comes to mind, a monk in India who tidied up the living quarters for all the other monks while they were practicing their meditation in the mornings. His gentle singing and beaming smile were indicators of how much he loved serving his brothers.

Then there was the Catholic priest I stayed with in Italy. He told me that he never felt closer to God than when he was consoling grieving families. It was the most difficult part of his job, he confessed, but also the most rewarding. Where most people shied away from such pain and felt uncomfortable, he had learned to be completely present with whatever arose in the process.

A Buddhist monastery and orphanage I stayed at in Thailand is another prime example. Being a part of the daily dedication that the monks put into raising and educating those unfortunate children was truly remarkable. Their effortless blend of joy and discipline was inspirational.

And how can I ever forget the 'casserole Christian ladies' in Georgia—that's what they called themselves. Whenever someone was sick, someone died, a new baby was born, or even when life just got a little hectic and busy, their team of devout Christian women showed up with casseroles and cakes to make sure that cooking wasn't one of the things that people had to worry about. Their service began within their congregation, but over the years, it spread to the broader community. Now, they even have a website where people can ask for assistance, but the work is always done in someone's home kitchen."

The monk nodded his head in amazement.

"The stories go on. In my four-decade journey, I have worked at countless food banks, soup kitchens, and clothes drives all around the world. Helping the needy is at the heart of what all the major religions do. In fact, all around the globe, service-based interfaith alliances have been created so that religious organizations can pool their resources and help the less fortunate with everything from healthcare to housing.

I have found that belonging to a community that values the perennial pursuit of goodness and is organized around service helps to get more people involved. That multiplies goodness in society."

Prayer

An elderly gentleman said: "You have prayed with people from all around the globe. What is the best way to pray?"

The monk answered with sincerity: "Prayers are personal conversations between us and the entities we direct them toward. They depend on our intentions. Therefore, before we pray, we should ask ourselves:

Do I want help with something?

Am I expressing gratitude?

Am I attempting to strengthen my bond?

Am I surrendering?

Am I praying for someone else?

Am I asking for blessings in general?

Do I wish to affirm my beliefs?

Is something else on my mind or in my heart?

After settling on an intention, we should be genuine. The words may be our own, or they may have been given to us by our tradition. Either way, we should make sure that what is expressed is also in our hearts—a prayer of integrity lines up thought, heart, and word in perfect harmony.

Then, we should pray with our feet.

In the end, our lives become our prayers."

Meditation

A young woman said: "I don't pray, but I do meditate. What are the most important things you've learned about meditation?"

The monk replied matter-of-factly: "There are four major elements included in all meditation traditions — *philosophy*, *doing*, *being*, and *support*. All of them are important.

Philosophy answers the question: Why meditate?

A Benedictine Christian monk told me that his reason for meditating was to experience the essence of religion as he understood it, to re-link with the origins of his creation, to be still with God.

A Hindu swami explained that, to him, meditation was evolution in reverse. Letting go of all the aspects of creation — body, mind, emotions, world — until nothing was left except that which is always present and never changes.

A Zen nun told me that the purpose of meditation was to notice whatever arises, to observe thoughts, not serve them tea.

And the most famous yogi of the 20th Century was guided by a simple question during meditation: What is behind the darkness of closed eyes?"

The monk briefly closed his eyes to illustrate.

"Once the philosophy, or why, has been established," he continued, "comes the doing part. The mechanics of meditation are near-universal. Practitioners sit, relax, and engage their minds. The main difference between traditions is how the mind is directed. Practitioners can focus on a single object, be led through a visualization process, or passively witness. I have found that all of them work.

Still, doing is mere preparation for being. For instance, when you prepare for sleep by lying down, getting comfortable, relaxing and letting your mind drift off, the goal of preparing for sleep is not the preparation but to fall asleep. If you count sheep, you don't wake yourself up to count sheep again after you fall asleep.

In the same way, once practitioners enter the being part of meditation—the meditative state; a passive state of silence that can best be described as *deep dreamless sleep while awake*—they don't focus on the doing practices again unless the mind becomes restless or disturbed.

These three steps are harder than they appear, which is why all the traditions emphasize the importance of support. Whether that comes in the form of teachers who have mastered the techniques or a group of practitioners sharing their experiences, getting feedback is paramount to continued practice and progress. It is odd, indeed, that we need support for something that we do in the recesses of our own minds, but on this the traditions agree.

Think of it this way. If you were making soup, *philosophy* would be the recipe, *doing* the cooking, *being* the tasting, and *support* would be getting feedback from other cooks after you told them how the soup tasted. Include these four perennial pillars in your meditation practice, and it will flourish."

Peace

A man said: "I am a warrior for justice. How can you talk of inner peace when there is no peace to be found in society?"

The monk responded with empathy: "The legendary founder of Taoism, Lao Tzu, wrote — six hundred years before the common era — that if we wanted to have peace in the world, we would need to have peace between nations; and that if we wanted to have peace in the nations, we needed to have peace in the cities; and if there was to be peace in the cities, we needed to have peace between neighbors; and if there was to be peace between neighbors, there needed to be peace at home; and, most importantly, if there was to be peace at home, there needed to be peace in the heart."

The monk placed both hands on his chest.

"Peace in the heart. That is where it all begins. Without peace in the heart, how can we expect to create peace in the home, between neighbors, in cities, in nations, in the world?"

The question hovered in the air for a moment before he continued.

"There is no contradiction. Taking part in a political struggle does not mean that one cannot also cultivate peace in the heart. Peace begets peace, and hatred begets hatred.

As a student of history, I know that revolutions have been known to devour their children. Once the powerless become powerful, their high-minded ideals can go by the wayside, and their thirst for vengeance get the better of them.

Living in South Africa with people who lived through the apartheid era provided me with a powerful example of the opposite. All of us know the story of Nelson Mandela, a man who spent 27 years in prison and emerged with an open heart. Had his longing been for revenge, the story would have ended very differently. It was only because he had cultivated peace in his heart that he could bring about a peaceful transfer of power.

So, organize and work towards your goals of social equity, but never, for one moment, think that the cultivation of peace in the heart is a waste of time. Peace in the heart is the only way to bring about peace in the world."

Holiness

A woman said: "I have to ask: Are you a holy man?"

The monk answered tentatively: "What is *holiness*? Is it a lifelong commitment to a spiritual path, a never-ending pursuit of goodness, an increasing feeling of oneness, an aspiration?

If yes, then I might be considered holy.

However, if holiness is total abstinence from desires, never thinking a bad thought, absolute self-control, mastery over the emotions, and all-around puritanism and perfection, then the answer is no."

The monk gathered his thoughts.

"Let me address the topic more broadly. Holiness rhymes with wholeness. Wholeness implies integrity, an alignment of thought, word, and deed. More people have fallen off imaginary pedestals of holiness because of discrepancies between what they *think*, what they *say*, and what they *do* than for any other reason.

When a person is whole, there is no need to pretend. If they don't know something, they say they don't know.

They don't pretend.

And when they are still working on achieving admirable qualities, they admit that.

They don't pretend.

A well-known yogi who was revered by his followers, once took me aside and told me that I should never buy into the mirage of my own holiness. He admitted to me that he stayed in his room half the day because people thought he was meditating all the time. He offered beautiful teachings, for sure, yet he was miserable because he could not be himself.

If holiness springs from integrity and wholeness, it is beautiful. If holiness springs from pretense, it poisons both the pretender and those who follow him.

In my travels, I have found that holiness never means perfection. Perfection is only for the Divine, not for humans. All holy men and women still need to go to the bathroom. All of them struggle with the limits of being human.

And yet, they provide us with inspiration. Their aspirations and dedication, their compassion and rich spiritual inner life, their tranquility and peace of mind are contagious. When they pluck the harmonious strings of their inner instruments, the melody it produces stirs something within. When they play their strings to the best of their ability, we are reminded of our own instruments. When their strings resonate with ours, it makes us aware of the possibilities that reside within.

My conclusion is that holiness that makes us feel small, weak, and dirty is not holiness at all. It is a display of superiority.

Real holiness nourishes our seeds of goodness.

Real holiness is free from pretense.

Real holiness aspires.

Real holiness inspires."

The Present

A young man said hurriedly: "All my friends keep telling me to slow down. What can I do to be more present, be in the moment, be in the now?"

The monk replied good-naturedly: "Let me set the record straight. You are always in the present. When you think about the past, you are in the present. When you think about the future, you are in the present. You cannot be anywhere else.

That said, you can learn to settle down and be more present in the present.

It is an acquired skill.

If you did not know how to ride a bike, I could teach you, but afterward, you would need to go home and practice based on those instructions. You would need to be okay with failing and falling before you mastered the skill of riding a bike. If you treat the following two instructions in the same way and go home and practice, you may gain the skill of being more present.

First, use the limitations of the body to your advantage. Whereas the mind can jump back and forth in time, the body can only be in the present. When you focus on bodily functions such as breathing, the sensation of air in your nostrils, your tongue touching the insides of your mouth, your heartbeat, and so on, your mind naturally anchors in the present moment.

Second, once you have successfully anchored your mind in the body, create a separate mental anchor. The mind is a tremendously powerful tool that can cause havoc when it lacks focus. A mental anchor is usually a word, a phrase, a mantra, or a prayer. It can also be a complex visual image, such as a beach, mountaintop, forest, or oasis, within which your mind can move freely. Whenever your mind is idle or disturbed, focus on your chosen word, image, prayer, or mantra. That will slow down your mind and help you focus.

With time and practice, you will be able to settle into each moment. That will be a gift for you and for the people you love."

There was a glint in the monk's eye as he concluded.

"There is no bigger present than being present in the present."

Mysticism

A middle-aged man asked: "What, if any, are the similarities between the mystical traditions?"

The monk answered with great gusto: "The mystery of life is impossible to explain. That is the true meaning of that word, *mystery*—something that is impossible to define or describe. It is not a puzzle or a problem like murder-mystery writers make it out to mean. What is mysterious is magnificent and truly incomprehensible to the human mind.

For instance, when we look at the night sky and know that each sparkly light on that dark canvas is a sun in its own right, we do not look at each other and say, I understand.

No.

Space is magnificent and mysterious.

So is life.

So is God.

Nevertheless, even though we cannot understand something fully, that doesn't mean we can't know more about it.

In that spirit, the experiential seekers of every tradition have approached the mysteries of God, Spirit, purpose, energy, life, and all the other mysteries for which we do not yet have the answers.

For this, they have used all of their faculties — body, emotions, senses, and mind — engaging in everything from shamanic journeys to ecstatic dancing to contemplation to prayer and meditation. When they have met the limits of their faculties, they have dared to go beyond the mind and body, thusly transcending their earthly limits."

The monk narrowed his eyes as if here were looking for the right words.

"Here comes the tricky part because people want clear answers.

After each journey of transcendence, seekers have returned to the limits of earthly life and have been left feeling like blind people who have momentarily gained sight and are trying to explain what a rainbow looks like to others who are still blind. What can words say about experiences beyond words?

That is why every mystic has encouraged us not to look at the finger but rather focus on where it is pointing. Words have merely pointed us in the direction. We must go on the journey.

First-hand examination of the mystery is what ties all of these mystical paths together. As with space explorers in the earthly realm, the mystical path has been reserved for those who've seen the limits of daily life and have been willing to go beyond. What instigates people to go on such journeys can be anything from a crash and burn event—where life is turned upside down—to an unexpected transcendental experience, an opening up to something that the senses cannot perceive.

Whenever people pause for long enough to peer beyond what is seen and heard, whenever they become enthralled by the sheer magnitude of life itself, they get a taste of the mystical.

Yet, only those few who keep going are true mystical explorers. In the same way that astronomers know that they can never know everything about space but keep exploring nevertheless, experiential seekers trek the unbeaten path with an increasing sense of humility, aware that the more they know about the mystery, the more mysterious it will become."

Religion and Science

A woman said: "I am both a scientist and a believer, yet both groups view me with suspicion. How can we reconcile the gap between science and religion?"

The monk replied wistfully: "Ideally, the two should complement each other.

Science is a powerful tool for natural exploration and advancement. It questions everything and demands third-party confirmation of data through repeatable experimentation. Yet, it has no inherent value system. It shows us what we can do, not whether we should do it.

Religious traditions are rich in value and require faith from their followers without providing evidence. They use mythical stories for teaching and are, therefore, by design, not always factual.

In a perfect world, science would explore, and wisdom traditions, including moral ones, such as humanism, could help believers figure out what to do with what has been discovered.

For instance, whenever science finds a cure for a malignant disease, we would ask ourselves, what does our value system tell us we should do with that cure? Should we give it to others? Sell it? Hide it? A clear value system would help us answer those questions."

The monk shook his head.

"Regrettably, that is not where we find ourselves. We are in the middle of a war of ideas with no end in sight. Like with any other war, we either continue until one side crushes the other—which would leave the world poorer as a result—or both sides will need to make concessions.

In recent years, I have met some of the finest minds trying to bridge this gap, and they have suggested some thought-provoking concessions as first steps.

On the religion side of the aisle, they've said that faith traditions would need to concede that when scientific data provides proof that differs from religious teachings, especially about the natural world, those teachings would need to change accordingly.

That may not be as difficult as it sounds, especially since most creation stories were never meant to be taken literally. In fact, most of them don't even need to be changed, only interpreted differently, which is what ministers and gurus alike do very well. "Let there be light," in the Bible could refer to the Big Bang. Brahma (the creator), Vishnu (the sustainer), and Shiva (the destroyer or transformer) in Hinduism could refer to the natural cycle of creation, sustenance, and destruction/transformation, and so on.

On the scientific side, for the purposes of peaceful coexistence and mutual respect, scientists would need to agree that there is more to the world than meets the eye—or any type of scientific equipment—and stop lampooning people of faith for beliefs that can neither be proven nor disproven. The very essence of faith is to believe in something that one cannot prove. Otherwise, it would not be faith.

These two concessions could serve as starting points. Nothing would happen overnight. It would take years, decades even, to institute such changes in academia and religious institutions around the globe. The progress would only occur on the coattails of willpower and consistent dialogue between the two sides. It would be challenging, but not impossible."

The monk raised his spirits and continued with optimism.

"However, let me suggest this. Instead of waiting for change, we can start right now. All of us in this room are interested in bettering the world.

Friends of faith, I urge you to practice your faith and then lead with your humanity in your interactions with people who do not believe as you do.

Show them what your values mean in everyday life. Show them that you care. And remember the words of Galileo, who said that we would not have been created with large brains and capacities for reason and research if God wanted us to forgo their use.

Friends of science, allow others to have faith in the unknown and present your facts to people with no scientific training in ways that can be understood. Instead of deriding their faith, see if you can make facts rhyme with their faith. Always be mindful that as science gets more complicated, people will need to take the outcome on faith in you and the scientific community. Be worthy of that faith.

Finally, we would do well to remember that not everyone is wrapped up in this perceived war between science and religion. I lived with a Muslim engineer and his family for several months, and he told me repeatedly that he saw it as his sacred duty to explore God's creation. The gap that some claim to be unbridgeable is already being bridged."

Traditions

A man shouted out: "Why all the looking back? Why such focus on old traditions? Can't we discard that luggage and be born anew into every moment? Can't we just live fully in the present?

The monk answered plainly: "Human society is built on traditions. Every culture has developed a buffet to help guide social interactions in everything from handshakes to marriage rituals. That should tell us something about their importance. If we were to throw out all the traditions, we would be discarding thousands of years of collective wisdom. For believers and mystics alike, traditions have served as vehicles for preserving important moral and spiritual truths.

The greatest paradox concerning traditions is that everything is continually changing. That is the nature of the dualistic world. It changes. Traditions, however, are resistant to change. That is their nature. They are inherently conservative, pushing against the natural order of the world.

Reconciling those immense forces is easier said than done. Some religions have created systems to allow for glacial changes by giving their leaders or a group of elder practitioners permission to make amendments, whereas others resist all change. Historically, absolute resistance has created rebels who have formed new religions and reformers who have revised religious traditions.

Buddha was a Hindu.

Jesus was a Jew.

Martin Luther and John Calvin were reformers.

Today, millions of people of every religion are quietly reforming traditions that have outlived their usefulness."

The monk raised his finger as if to caution the group.

"The key during reformation and renewal is to understand that each tradition is there for a reason. Before we make changes, we must first understand the purpose of the tradition. If it is central to the culture and belief system, then we should tread carefully. If it is peripheral, we can make changes more readily.

There are important reasons why traditions have survived. They serve a purpose in our lives. If we threw every prayer, every ritual, every meditation technique, and every moral code out the window, it would be our loss.

Yet, you also speak the truth. Being born anew into each moment is the yin to the yang of traditions. We must learn to balance the two in our spiritual lives."

Oneness

An older man said: "You have sparked my interest. Can you better explain what you mean by oneness?"

The monk responded graciously: "There appear to be three significant sensations of oneness common to all the spiritual traditions.

They are *symbiosis*, *unity*, and *non-duality*.

Symbiosis refers to the interconnectedness of all worldly things. Through practices such as meditation, shamanic rituals, and nature walks, people have reported feelings of interconnectedness, of sensing how everything is connected to everything else. This feeling of symbiosis goes further than an intellectual understanding of the cycle of life. It is like tapping into the central nervous system of creation. Those who have had this experience often talk about the Earth as one body. It profoundly influences their interactions with other people and with nature.

Unity refers to such a close connection that there hardly seems to be a separation. Think of the yin/ yang symbol as a representation. People periodically experience this feeling in earthly relationships. Still, it is more common during spiritual practices like prayer and meditation where people report such a close relationship with God that they can hardly make a distinction. The two have merged into a single entity, united. The experiencer uses phrases like, "I was one with God," implying a subtle separation even though the relationship is as close as it can ever get. Sensations of unity often create feelings of bliss and ecstasy. Loneliness disappears and is replaced with a sense of supreme connection.

Non-duality is the purest form of oneness. In that state, all sense of separation disappears. There is only one. The profoundness of this experience cannot be understated. It like a drop returning to the ocean, merging with the essence from which it originated, having no ability to discern itself from other drops or the ocean itself. If the drop is ever separated again—as most spiritual seekers are when they return to the waking state—it will carry with it the memory of the ocean. There will always be ocean in the drop. The sense of non-duality will remain in duality.

Symbiosis.

Unity.

Non-duality.

All are valid experiences of oneness, a philosophy that has been expressed by Zen Buddhists, Christian mystics, universal Sufis, Native American medicine men, Taoist masters, Hindu swamis, Jewish Kabbalists, nonreligious physicists, and many more.

Lift the veil and see.

All is one. One is all."

Interfaith

A middle-aged woman said: "You speak of mingling with people of other faiths. Will that not dilute our own faith in the process?"

The monk answered with compassion: "The primary goal of interfaith work is *harmony*. For that purpose, we need a combination of confidence and curiosity.

We need confidence in our own faith so that we won't fear being exposed to other ideas and faith practices. I have found that believers who fear dilution lack confidence.

We need curiosity to expand our knowledge of creation and the people who inhabit this planet. Curiosity leads to questions. What do other people believe? How do they practice their beliefs? What commonalities do we have based on our shared humanity? How can we better live together?

When we are equipped with confidence and curiosity, interfaith work will allow us to honor differences and celebrate similarities. The outcome is beautiful. When we can see ourselves reflected in our neighbors of different faiths, we can truly love our neighbors as ourselves."

The monk's smiling face turned contemplative.

"Among all the faith traditions that I have been associated with, there are hundreds of differences. Different customs, rituals, stories, prophets, ceremonies… the list goes on.

Anyone who claims that all religions are the same has never looked closely.

I honor those differences, but I do not celebrate them. I celebrate the similarities.

That is how I have been able to assimilate. How I have, more often than not, been counted as a valued member of groups I have stayed with. In every community of believers that has graciously taken me in, I have looked for and affirmed important likenesses. When I've seen them in others, others have seen them in me.

Some people don't seem to understand this, but every celebration of diversity creates subtle divisions. When I acknowledge that you come from a different culture, a different background, and a different race, we underline those differences, and divisions remain. Whenever I see you from then on, I am reminded of how different we are.

There is another approach.

We could do exactly the same thing, honor each other's culture, background, and race, but then move on to explore and celebrate similarities. Afterward, parallels would remain. When we'd see each other again, we would be reminded of our likenesses.

That is why, every time I meet someone new, I look that person in the eye and say with the utmost sincerity, I am your brother.

After that has been made clear, we can discuss differences, but I find that starting with similarities generally sets the tone for peaceful interactions.

We are all brothers and sisters, all part of the same human family. Reminding ourselves of that is the essential work of interfaith relations."

Death

An old man said: "My time is soon approaching. Can you talk to us about death?"

The monk replied serenely: "There is no greater mystery than death. Ever since humans became conscious of their own mortality, they have asked questions.

What happens after death?

Is this all there is?

Will I go to Heaven or Hell?

Will I be born again in another form?

The truth is, we don't know.

Beliefs about what happens after death need to be taken on faith alone.

Therefore, I cannot tell you what to believe.

All I can say is this. What you believe about death will greatly influence how you live your life. Fear of death will turn into fear of life.

Having worked side-by-side with people of all faiths as they have comforted the dying, I can tell you that tremendous peace has descended on all those who have accepted their fate, no matter their religion.

Don't wait until your dying day. Use your faith to make peace with your mortality.

Then live your life fully."

Life's Purpose

A young woman asked: "What have you learned about life's purpose on your journey?

The monk responded attentively: "As with death, life's purpose depends on the central tenets of your belief system.

If your belief system is Earth-centered, life's purpose is to get the most out of life.

If your belief system is value-centered, life's purpose is to live a life based on those values.

If your belief system is non-duality-centered, life's purpose is to fully merge with the One without a Second and relinquish the separate self.

If your belief system is God-centered, life's purpose is to worship God in all possible ways.

I have seen these beliefs and more lived vivaciously and with joy. The variety is great. If there is a single purpose to life, I have not identified it in my journeys.

However, I have found that having a purpose is tremendously important. It adds stride to your step and taps into the energy of your soul.

You can find your life's purpose by connecting with what you believe in your heart of hearts. Whether that leads you to trek the path less traveled or to take the road well-paved as laid out by people in your faith community, ultimately, the choice is yours."

Final Words

The room fell silent when everyone had asked their questions. The monk offered his closing remarks: "I want to thank you. You came here with open minds and open hearts. From what I have seen, you are sincere seekers.

If any of you have fallen in love with *perennialism*, like I did, please know that we have hardly scratched the surface. The expedition you will embark upon is one of first-hand discovery. Don't read endless travel brochures and wait at the train station. Take the trip. Find out for yourself. If a certain meditation technique intrigues you, try it. If a certain prayer rings true, repeat it. If certain moral structures appeal to you, follow them. Do so with open eyes and seek understanding. Following blindly is not part of the perennial journey. It is one of self-reliance. You may uncover what I have found or discover something completely different. That is the beauty of the search.

To those of you who have expanded your horizons during our time together, but will continue to follow the traditions you were raised in, or the ones you have chosen as adults, I say, *be authentic*. I have lived among the faithful all my life. There is beauty in every tradition. Simply remember to guard against the kicking by remaining aware of the relationship between attraction and repulsion. Never allow your love for one tradition to turn into hate for another. As you interact with people of other faiths, honor diversity while you celebrate similarities. Beliefs may differ, but we are all human. All of us are brothers and sisters."

The monk arose, smiled broadly, placed his hands in a prayer position, bowed from his waist, and bid farewell.

"May peace be with you."

Acknowledgments

I cannot take credit for all of the ideas that the monk spoke of in this book. His voice echoes the teachings of Huston Smith, Aldous Huxley, Wayne Teasdale, Ken Wilber, and other great thinkers in the realm of religion and perennial philosophy. The character is fictional, but the wisdom is real.

I took inspiration and quotes from a wide variety of scriptures, and included some of the teachings I received at All Faiths Seminary, especially from Rev. Jon Mundy, a mystic in his own right. Furthermore, I made sure that stories about acts of kindness were based on actual events.

Kahlil Gibran provided me with the structure for this book in his seminal work, *The Prophet*, which I carried around with me for years as a source of inspiration.

Last but not least, it was my father, Guðlaugur Bergmann (1938-2004), who ignited the perennial spark in me with his interest in theosophy, mysticism, and spiritualism. I miss him dearly.

Gudjon Bergmann, 2021

About the Author

Gudjon Bergmann is an Icelandic-American author, interfaith minister, bridge-builder, and amateur musician. Visit his website or social media pages to learn more.

www.gudjonbergmann.com
www.facebook.com/bergmanngudjon
www.twitter.com/gudjonbergmann

Made in the USA
Monee, IL
04 July 2021

61e1c52b-f512-463d-af8e-09f558d8f691R01